# Fair Dinkum
# AUSSIE CHRISTMAS

Bucko & Champs • Kilmeny Niland

A Scholastic Press book from Scholastic Australia

Bucko & Champs dedicate this book to all who celebrate a fair dinkum summertime
Aussie Christmas under the Southern Cross—and who love to sing about it!          CB, GC

For two Aussie musicians—my brother, Patrick, & Patrick, my son.                    KN

Scholastic Press
345 Pacific Highway
Lindfield NSW 2070
An imprint of Scholastic Australia Pty Limited (ABN 11 000 614 577)
PO Box 579 Gosford NSW 2250
www.scholastic.com.au

Part of the Scholastic Group
Sydney • Auckland • New York • Toronto • London • Mexico City
• New Delhi • Hong Kong • Buenos Aires • Puerto Rico

First published by Scholastic Australia in 2007.
This edition published in 2012.
All words by Colin Buchanan and Greg Champion except 'Fair Dinkum Twelve Days of Aussie
Christmas' words by Colin Buchanan.
© Universal Music Publishing Australia; Orient Pacific Music/ORiGiN except 'Fair Dinkum
Twelve Days of Aussie Christmas' © Universal Music Publishing Australia P/L.
Illustrations copyright © Kilmeny Niland, 2007.

A catalogue record for this book is available from the National Library of Australia.

ISBN 978-1-74283-570-9 (pbk.)

Typeset in Papyrus.

Printed in China by RR Donnelley.
Scholastic Australia's policy, in association with RR Donnelley, is to use papers that are
renewable and made efficiently from wood grown in sustainable forests, so as to minimise its
environmental footprint.

10 9 8 7 6 5 4 3 2 1                                    12 13 14 15 16 / 1

# Fair Dinkum AUSSIE CHRISTMAS

## Contents

All words by Colin Buchanan and Greg Champion
except † words by Colin Buchanan

# Deck the Shed with Bits of Wattle

Deck the shed with bits of wattle

Fa La La La La La La La La

Whack some gumleaves in a bottle

Fa La La La La La La La La

All the shops are open Sundies

Fa La La La La La La La La

Buy your Dad some socks and undies

Fa La La La La La La La La

Deck the shed with bits of gumtree
Hang some deco's off the plum tree
Plant some kisses on the missus
Have a ripper Aussie Christmas!

Say g'day to friends and rellies
Wave them off with bulging bellies
Kids and babies, youngies, oldies
May your fridge be full of coldies

5

Chop the wood and stoke the barbie
Ring the folks in Abu Dhabi
Pop the stuffing in the turkey
Little Mary's feeling ercky!

Rally, rally round the table
Fill your belly while you're able
Joyce and Joany, Dave and Daryl
Sing an Aussie Christmas Carol!

# We Wish You a Ripper Christmas

*Chorus*
We wish you a ripper Christmas
A full-bore ripper Christmas
A dead-set ripper Christmas
And a snappy New Year

May the kids have a hoot
May the pressies be beaut
From the big-bellied fella
In the red and white suit

*Chorus*

Send cards through the post
Have a big Christmas roast
Then hitch up the caravan
And shoot down the coast

*Chorus*

Great pressies we bring
All wrapped up with string
They're not very expensive
But they're interesting

*Chorus*

Jingle Bells, Batman smells
Robin flew away
Billy Bunter did a grunter
Flying TAA

With candles alight
And faces so bright
We'll sing lots of carols
Long into the night

*Chorus*

We'll hang up the holly
Be cheerful and jolly
And fill up our tum-tums
With lolly after lolly

*Chorus*

# 🇦🇺 C'mon, it's an Aussie Christmas 🇦🇺

*Chorus*
C'mon it's an Aussie Christmas
From Boyup Brook to Streaky Bay
C'mon it's an Aussie Christmas
Roll on Aussie Christmas Day
C'mon it's an Aussie Christmas
Grab the rellies, call your mates
And have yourselves a ripper little
Aussie Christmas Day

AUSSIE CHRISTMAS DAY!

Score the meat from Ronny Kissell's
A ham from Poppy's Delico
Get a bag of pre-cut coleslaw
Hit the drive-thru bottlo

Top the tank of barbie gas up
A monster bag of salted chips
Get a box of daggy bonbons
A good French onion dip

*Chorus*

11

Trim the lawn and do the edges
Get the doggie an extra bone
Whack a tarp between the gumtrees
Speakers on the patio

Bags of ice from Johnno's Garage
Scattered chairs around the yard
Grab the neighbours, crank the hi-fi
Then knuckle down and party hard

*Chorus*

##  We Three Kings

We three kings of Bankstown Square
Selling Grandpa's underwear
So fantastic, no elastic
Twenty cents a pair

# Fair Dinkum Twelve Days of Aussie Christmas

On the first day of Christmas a swagman at the gate
Said, Have a ripper Aussie Christmas, mate!

On the second day of Christmas an emu by the fence
Said, Good onya, cob
Have a ripper Aussie Christmas, mate!

On the third day of Christmas a shearer down the shed
Said, How 'bout the flies?
Good onya, cob
Have a ripper Aussie Christmas, mate!

On the fourth day of Christmas a goanna on a rock
Said, It's stinkin' hot
How 'bout the flies?
Good onya, cob
Have a ripper Aussie Christmas, mate!

15

On the fifth day of Christmas Frank put up the sign
Total Fire Ban
It's stinkin' hot
How 'bout the flies?
Good onya, cob
Have a ripper Aussie Christmas, mate!

On the sixth day of Christmas a dingo by the dam
Said, I'm flat out till Chrissy
Total Fire Ban
It's stinkin' hot
How 'bout the flies?
Good onya, cob
Have a ripper Aussie Christmas, mate!

On the seventh day of Christmas Sue put up the lights
Drop in for a chinwag
I'm flat out till Chrissy
Total Fire Ban
It's stinkin' hot
How 'bout the flies?
Good onya, cob
Have a ripper Aussie Christmas, mate!

On the eighth day of Christmas they called the CFA
Santa's on a fire truck
Drop in for a chinwag
Flat out till Chrissy
Total Fire Ban
It's stinkin' hot
How 'bout the flies?
Good onya, cob
Have a ripper Aussie Christmas, mate!

On the ninth day of Christmas
You should have heard the cheer
School's out for summer!
Santa's on a fire truck
Drop in for a chinwag
Flat out till Chrissy
Total Fire Ban
It's stinkin' hot
How 'bout the flies?
Good onya, cob
Have a ripper Aussie Christmas, mate!

On the tenth day of Christmas y'couldn't move in town
A madhouse up Main Street
School's out for summer!
Santa's on a fire truck
Drop in for a chinwag
Flat out till Chrissy
Total Fire Ban
It's stinkin' hot
How 'bout the flies?
Good onya, cob
Have a ripper Aussie Christmas, mate!

On the eleventh day of Christmas they drew the raffle prize
You little beauty!
Madhouse up Main Street
School's out for summer!
Santa's on a fire truck
Drop in for a chinwag
Flat out till Chrissy
Total Fire Ban
It's stinkin' hot
How 'bout the flies?
Good onya, cob
Have a ripper Aussie Christmas, mate!

On the twelfth day of Christmas we'll take an early mark
Knock off till New Year
You little beauty!
Madhouse up Main Street
School's out for summer!
Santa's on a fire truck
Drop in for a chinwag
Flat out till Chrissy
Total Fire Ban
It's stinkin' hot
How 'bout the flies?
Good onya, cob
Have a ripper Aussie Christmas, mate!

#  The Feral Pig and Cane Toad

The holly and the ivy
If they come up in your yard
Then go and get the Roundup
And hit the mongrels hard

The feral pig and cane toad
Have a right to exist
But they don't fit our ecology
And make awful Christmas gifts

The rabbit is a dreadful pest
And introduced, of course
But it makes a bonzer Christmas dish
With gravy and plum sauce

The privet and lantana
Are an absolute eyesore
And whoever introduced them
Has a lot to answer for

The banksia and bottlebrush
Koala and emu
They are honest Aussie diggers
They're the only ones true blue

The holly and the ivy
If they come up in your yard
Then go and get the Roundup
And hit the mongrels hard

21

## ☆ There's Nothing More Like Christmas ☆

*Chorus*
You can't have a summer without Christmas
You can't have a Christmas without heat
You can't have a kiss without the mistletoe
And a barbie's not a barbie unless you burn the meat
But if you've got the nibblies and the crackers
It's stinkin' hot and clearly summertime
The flies, the food, the rellies and the pressies
Then bless my soul, it must be Christmas time

There's nothing more like Christmas than a pre-school pageant
And shepherds with bath towels and faces all aglow
There's nothing like a Santa with a pillow for a belly
Chuckin' lollies to the kiddies with a HO HO HO!

*Chorus*

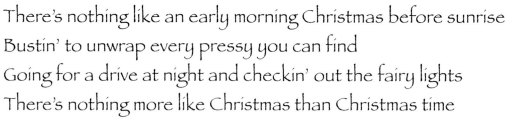

There's nothing like an early morning Christmas before sunrise
Bustin' to unwrap every pressy you can find
Going for a drive at night and checkin' out the fairy lights
There's nothing more like Christmas than Christmas time

But if you've got the nibblies and the crackers
It's stinkin' hot and clearly summertime
The flies, the food, the rellies and the pressies
Then bless my soul, it must be Christmas time

## He's the Aussie Santa

He drives a ute with a big V8
He's the Aussie Santa
He's everybody's mate
He's the Aussie Santa
He's the fat bloke in the Akubra
With the Blunnies and the dusty grin
And he'll roll through town this Christmas
And the bush folks all love him

*Chorus*
He's the Aussie Santa—hey hey hey
He's the Aussie Santa—ho ho ho
He's the Aussie Santa—look at him go
He's the Aussie Santa

25

He's caught barra in the Kimberley
He's the Aussie Santa
He's been a ringer up at VRD
He's the Aussie Santa
He's driven road trains right
Through the west
But he still loves his Christmas gig the best
He's not so big on the 'ho ho ho'
He says 'Onya, Digger, wad'ya know?'

*Chorus*

He's got the ute choc
Full of Christmas cheer
And he hits the outback every year
He's got a load of pressies
And it's his shout
He'll make sure the bush kids
Don't miss out

*Chorus*

#  Good Old Wally King

Good old Wally King looked out
On his crop of barley
'Bless my soul and blow me down
That looks to me like Charlie
Haven't seen him round these parts
Many a long year
Reckon I might offer him
A glass of Christmas cheer'

'Agnes put the kettle on
Quick as you are able
Let us make another place
For him at the table
He looks a little worse for wear
His clothes are old and baggy
It's a long and weary road
For an honest swaggie'

Mates they'd been in years before
Now the two were older
And so he welcomed Charlie in
Hand upon his shoulder
Gladly those three feasted there
And in the warmth of sharing
The Christmas season brought again
A time of peace and caring

29

## Australians Let Us Barbecue

Australians let us barbecue for Christmas time is here

A time to stop and rest a bit, and psych up for New Year

On patterned plastic tablecloth we'll eat our pudding up

And drink a Christmas cordial in polystyrene cup

30

Australians let us barbecue for Christmas time is come
The time we sing that silly song 'Pa Ruppa Pum Pum Pum'
We'll fa la la and ho ho ho, and all that Christmas stuff
We'll crack a gag with Pop and Gran, and chuckle our heads off

Australians let us go for broke in backyards great and small
With Christmas gifts and outdoor chairs, with cricket bat and ball
We'll pass the salad dressing round, we'll eat potato chips
And compliment the hostess on a great French onion dip
With sausages and coleslaw too, then let us barbecue